KU-166-536

This
Treasure Cove Story
belongs to

_____

THE LUCKY PUPPY

A CENTUM BOOK 978-1-912396-26-9
Published in Great Britain by Centum Books Ltd.
This edition published 2018. 1 3 5 7 9 10 8 6 4 2

Copyright © 2018 Disney Enterprises, Inc. All rights reserved.

Based on the book *The Hundred and One Dalmatians* by Dodie Smith,
published by The Viking Press.

No part of this publication may be reproduced, stored in a retrieval
system, or transmitted in any form or by any means, electronic,
mechanical, photocopying, recording or otherwise without
the prior permission of the publishers.

Centum Books Ltd, 20 Devon Square, Newton Abbot,
Devon, TQ12 2HR, UK.

www.centumbooksltd.co.uk | books@centumbooksltd.co.uk
CENTUM BOOKS Limited Reg.No. 07641486.

A CIP catalogue record for this book is available
from the British Library.

Printed in China.

centum

A Treasure Cove Story

WALT DISNEY'S
The Lucky Puppy

BY JANE WERNER WATSON
ILLUSTRATED BY THE WALT DISNEY STUDIO
ADAPTED BY ALLEN HUBBARD AND DON BESTOR

Lucky the puppy lived with his father, Pongo, his mother, Perdita, and with all his sisters and brothers. The people who belonged to them were Roger and Anita and Nanny Cook. (That's Nanny Cook in the doorway above.)

Here are Penny and Lenny, Salter and Pepper, Jolly and Rolly and Patch and Latch.

Here are Spot and Dot,
Blob and Blot, Blackie and Whitey
and – where's Lucky?

Here's Lucky. He's in front
of the television watching his
favourite show, *Thunderbolt*.

Whenever Penny and
Lenny wanted to dig holes…

or Salter and Pepper
wanted to chew bones…

or Patch and Latch
wanted to chase tails...

or Jolly and Rolly wanted to jump
at Nanny Cook's apron strings...

or Spot and Dot wanted to play hide-and-seek…

or Blob and Blot wanted to growl at the mirror…

or Blackie and Whitey wanted to take a nap,

Lucky never joined in. He just wanted to sit
in front of the television watching *Thunderbolt*.

Or he practised tricks he saw on television. 'I'm going to be a television star,' said Lucky.

Well, all the other puppies
learned puppy tricks. Soon
they could sit up and roll over.

They could dance
and shake hands.

They could jump for a treat
and walk politely on a lead.

But not Lucky. He was too busy
dreaming about being a television star.

One day, he decided he was ready to be in a television show. So he slipped out of the house and ran down the street.

He ran around a corner. And there he stopped. He was lost. He didn't know his way to the television studio. And he didn't know his way home.

Poor Lucky. He walked and walked and walked. He tried to show people his television tricks. But they didn't understand.

'He doesn't seem to know any regular puppy tricks,' the people said.

Finally, a policeman came
along. He looked at Lucky's tag.
And he took Lucky home.

There were Penny and Lenny,
Salter and Pepper, Jolly and Rolly,
Patch and Latch,

Spot and Dot, Blob and Blot
and Blackie and Whitey, all
doing puppy tricks for treats.
But not Lucky.

Lucky was all tired out.

He crept straight into his basket.

And he went to sleep.

He even slept through the *Thunderbolt* show while the other puppies watched.

But the next morning, Lucky was up bright and early. 'Time enough for television later,' he said. 'Now I am going to learn my puppy tricks.' And he did!

Treasure Cove Stories

1 Three Little Pigs
2 Snow White
& The Seven Dwarfs
3 The Fox and the Hound
- Hide and Seek
4 Dumbo
5 Cinderella
6 Cinderella's Friends
7 Alice In Wonderland
8 Mad Hatter's Tea Party
from Alice In Wonderland
9 Mickey Mouse and
his Spaceship
10 Peter Pan
11 Pinocchio
12 Mickey Mouse Flies
the Christmas Mail
13 Sleeping Beauty
and the Good Fairies
14 The Lucky Puppy
15 Chicken Little
16 Mother Goose
17 Coco
18 Winnie-the-Pooh and Tigger
19 The Sword in the Stone
20 Mary Poppins
21 The Jungle Book
22 Aristocats
23 Lady and the Tramp
24 Bambi
25 Bambi - Friends
of the Forest
26 Pete's Dragon
27 Beauty & The Beast
- The Teapot's Tale
28 Monsters, Inc.
- M is for Monster
29 Finding Nemo
30 The Incredibles
31 The Incredibles
- Jack-Jack Attack
32 Ratatouille
- Your Friend the Rat
33 Wall-E
34 Up
35 Princess and the Frog

36 Toy Story - The Pet Problem
37 Dora the Explorer - Dora and
the Unicorn King
38 Dora the Explorer
- Grandma's House
39 Spider-Man
- Night of the Vulture!
40 Wreck-it Ralph
41 Brave
42 The Invincible Iron Man
- Eye of the Dragon
43 SpongeBob SquarePants
- Sponge in Space!
44 SpongeBob SquarePants
- Where the Pirates Arrrgh!
45 Toy Story - A Roaring
Adventure
46 Cars - Deputy Mater
Saves the Day!
47 Spider-Man
- Trapped By The Green Goblin
48 Big Hero 6
49 Spider-Man - High Voltage!
50 Frozen
51 Cinderella Is My Babysitter
52 Beauty & The Beast
- I Am The Beast
53 Blaze and the Monster
Machines - Mighty Monster
Machines
54 Blaze and the Monster
Machines - Dino Parade!
55 Teenage Mutant Ninja Turtles
- Follow The Ninja!
56 I Am A Princess
57 Paw Patrol
- The Big Book of Paw Patrol
58 Paw Patrol
- Adventures with Grandpa
59 Merida Is My Babysitter
60 Trolls
61 Trolls Holiday Special
62 The Secret Life of Pets
63 Zootropolis
64 Ariel Is My Babysitter
65 Inside Out

66 Belle Is My Babysitter
67 The Lion Guard
- Eye In The Sky
68 Moana
69 Finding Dory
70 Guardians of the Galaxy
71 Captain America
- High-Stakes Heist!
72 Ant-Man
73 The Mighty Avengers
74 The Mighty Avengers
- Lights Out!
75 The Incredible Hulk
76 Shimmer & Shine
- Wish upon a Sleepover
77 Shimmer & Shine
- Backyard Ballet
78 Paw Patrol - All-Star Pups!
79 Teenage Mutant Ninja Turtles
- Really Spaced Out!
80 Cars 2 - Travel Buddies
81 Madagascar
82 Jasmine Is My Babysitter
83 How To Train Your Dragon
84 Shrek
85 Puss In Boots
86 Kung Fu Panda
87 Beauty & The Beast
- I Am Belle
88 The Lion Guard
- The Imaginary Okapi
89 Thor - Thunder Strike
90 Guardians of the Galaxy
-Rocket to the Rescue
91 Nella The Princess Knight
- Nella and the Dragon
92 Shimmer & Shine
- Treasure Twins!
93 Olaf's Frozen Adventure
94 Black Panther
95 Branch's Bunker Birthday
96 Shimmer & Shine
- Pet Talent Show

Book list may be subject to change.

An ongoing series to collect and enjoy!